TANGRAMS

JON MILLINGTON

Thinker

PUZZLE PICTURES
TO MAKE YOU THINK!

TARQUIN PUBLICATIONS

WHERE ARE THE TANGRAM PIECES?

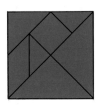

At the centre of this book you will find some card Tangram pieces to cut out. They come in two colours and two sizes. But remember!
You only use *one* set at a time and you *must* use all seven pieces.

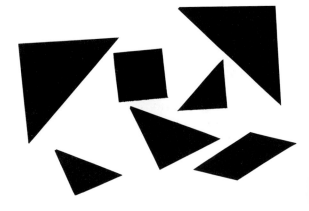

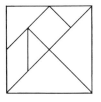

You will see from this diagram that it is easy to draw a new set of Tangrams on any suitable card. Simply start with a square, or trace the design from the front cover.
It is also possible to buy very nice sets of Tangrams made out of mahogany and to use them to solve the puzzles.

At the back of this book there is a special envelope to cut out and make. It glues back into the book on a special tab and is used to store the Tangram pieces until you need them.

© 1986 JON MILLINGTON
I.S.B.N. 0 906212 56 1
DESIGN: PAUL CHILVERS
PRINTING: THE FIVE CASTLES PRESS

TARQUIN PUBLICATIONS
STRADBROKE
DISS
NORFOLK IP21 5JP
ENGLAND

If you would like an up-to-date catalogue of other Tarquin books, please write to the publisher at the address above.

IS IT AN ANCIENT CHINESE PUZZLE?

Probably the answer is yes, but it is not certain. No-one really knows when it first appeared or why it is so called. The name Tangram may come from "Tang", the word for Chinese in some parts of China (in honour of the period of their history known as the Tang Dynasty), and "gram" meaning something written (as in telegram or diagram). Chinese books of Tangram designs were published at the beginning of the last century, but the puzzle itself probably existed long before then and is now known all over the world.

Why so many interesting outlines can be made from these seven particular shapes, no-one knows, but it is undoubtedly true that they can. Tangrams are almost the exact opposite of a jig-saw puzzle. Instead of many complicated pieces fitting together in only one way, these seven simple pieces can be fitted together in many, many different ways.

Try arranging the seven pieces to make each puzzle picture in this book. Some are easy, but others will certainly make you think. Try also to make interesting new designs of your own.

I should like to thank my wife and Jane, Libby and Susan for all their help with this book.

J.M. Bristol.

Use just one Tangram set to make each shape.
You must use all seven pieces.

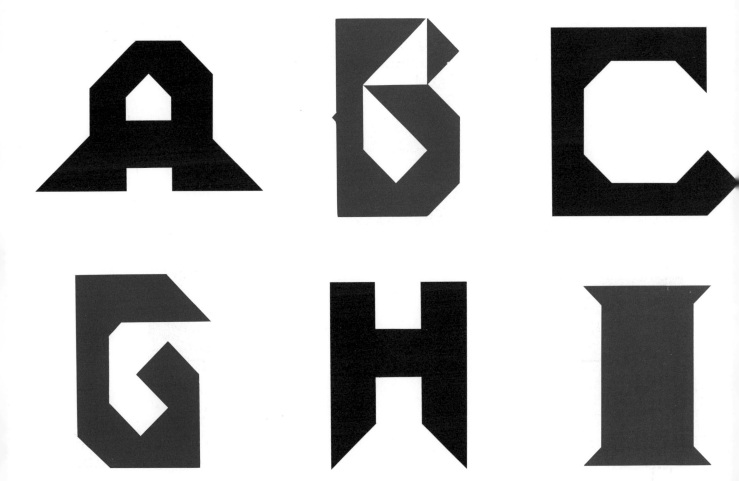

D E F

J K L

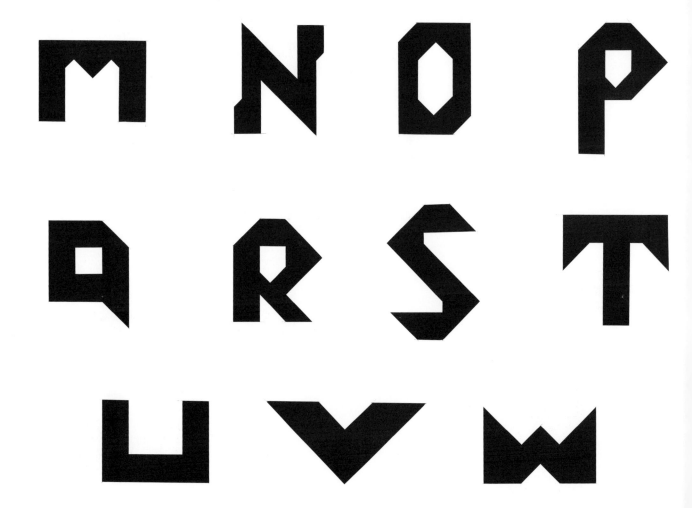

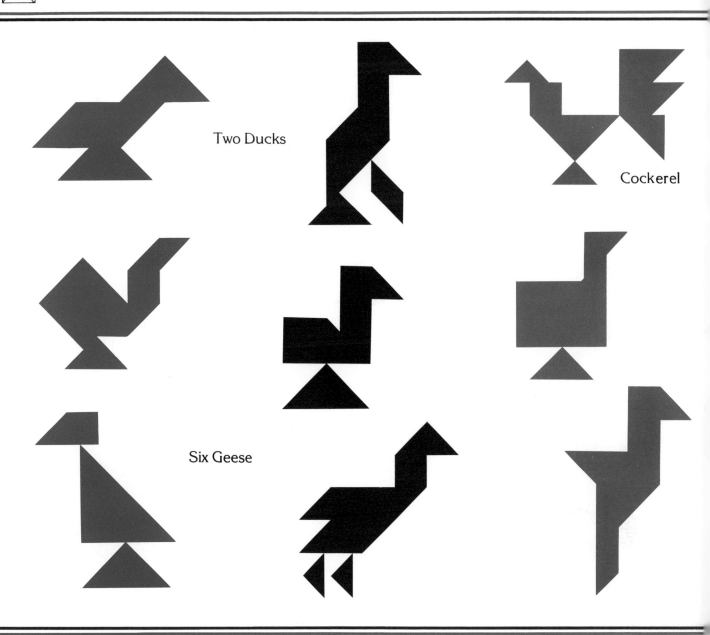

Two Ducks

Cockerel

Six Geese

Three Chicks

Penguin

Vulture

Ostrich

Pelican

Eagle

Puffin

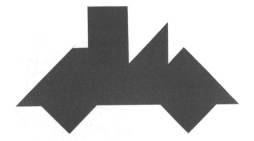

Pedal Car

Tank

Invalid Car

Steam Train

Space Craft

Lorry

Aeroplane

Rocket

Use just one Tangram set to make each shape.
You must use all seven pieces.

Postman

Lady

Priest

Girl

Boy Reading

Dancer

Girl in Cape

Angel

Praying

Chinese Coolie

Thinker

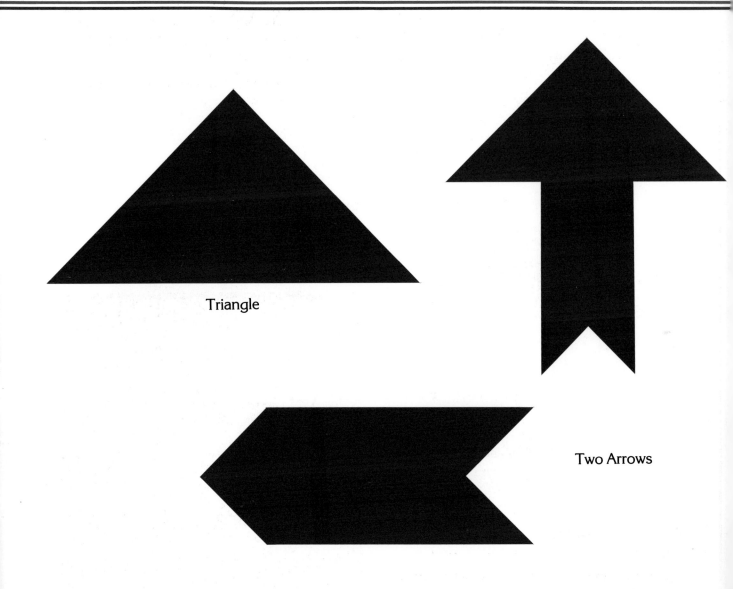

Triangle

Two Arrows

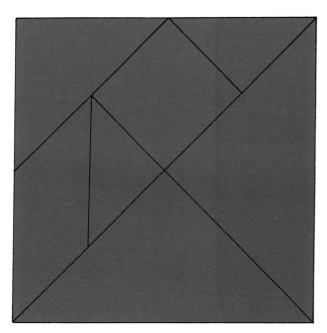

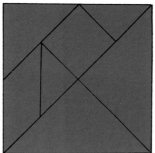

Each person needs just one set of pieces to try to solve a Tangram puzzle.

Here you have a choice of two different sizes and two different colours.

Cut out the sets of pieces and then store them in the special envelope until they are needed.

Up to four people can puzzle at the same time, using one set each.

CUT ALONG THIS LINE

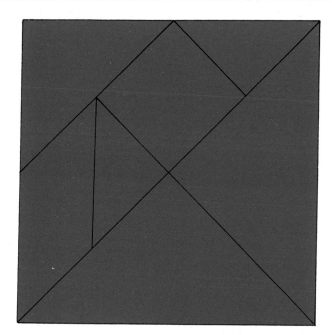

Each person needs just one set of pieces to try to solve a Tangram puzzle.

Here you have a choice of two different sizes and two different colours.

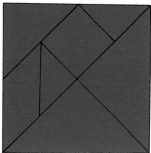

Cut out the sets of pieces and then store them in the special envelope until they are needed.

Up to four people can puzzle at the same time, using one set each.

CUT ALONG THIS LINE

Parallelogram

Rectangle

Trapezium

Isosceles Trapezium

Pentagon

Hexagon

The colours give a clue as to which shape goes where.
Just use seven pieces which would form a square.

Camel Lying Down

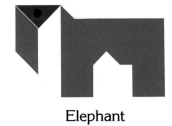

Elephant

Polar Bear

Seal with Ball

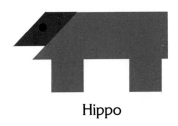

Hippo

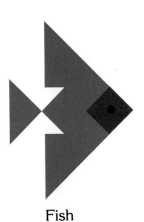

Fish

THESE ANIMALS SEEM EVEN STRANGER THAN I DO

Loch Ness Monster

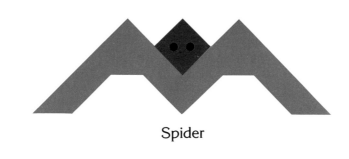

Spider

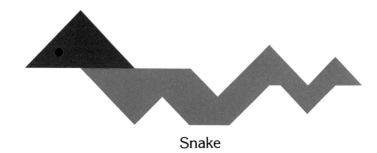

Snake

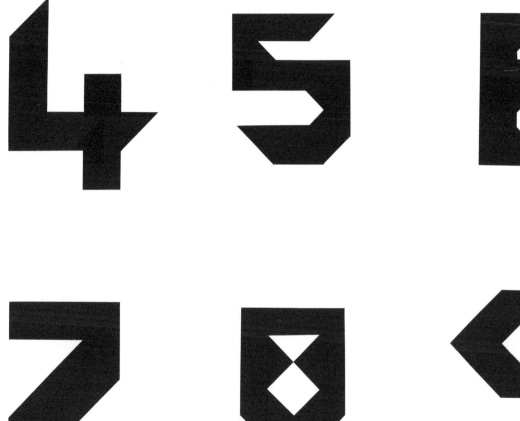

Use just one Tangram set to make each shape.
You must use all seven pieces.

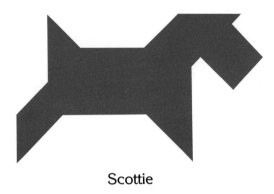

Scottie

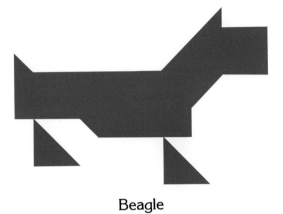

Beagle

Airedale

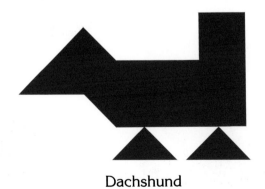

Dachshund

18

Lying Down

Sleeping

Sitting Up

Jumping Up

Jumping Down

Cautious

Manx

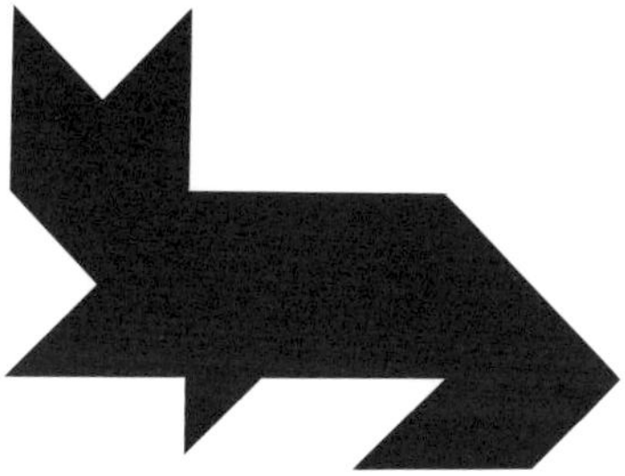

Curled Up

Resting

The colours give a clue as to which shape goes where.
Just use seven pieces which would form a square.

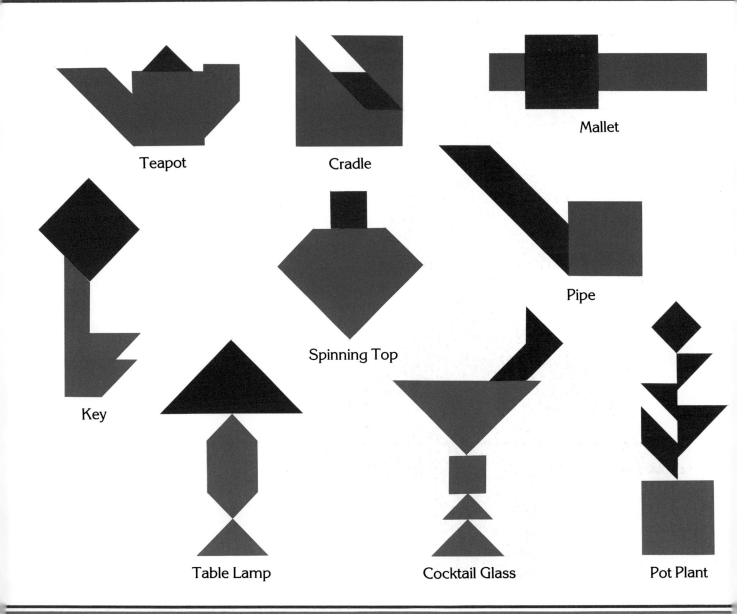

Teapot

Cradle

Mallet

Key

Spinning Top

Pipe

Table Lamp

Cocktail Glass

Pot Plant

Pram

Tree

A B C D E F G H

I J K L M N O P Q

R S T U V W

Page 6

X
Y
Z

Page 2,3,4,5

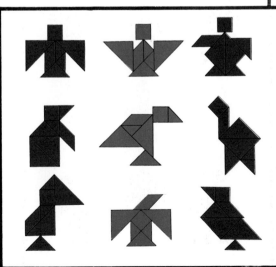

Page 7

22

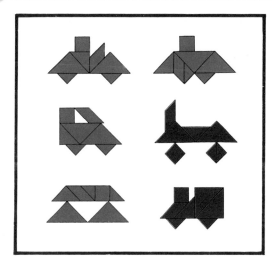

Page 8

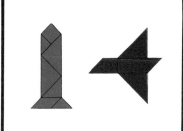

Page 9

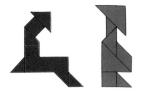

Page 11

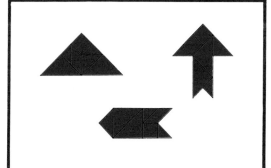

Page 12

Page 10

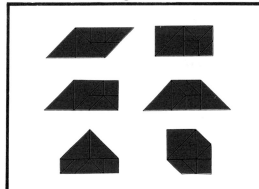

Page 13

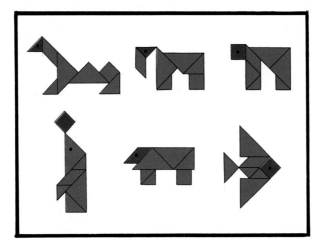

Page 14

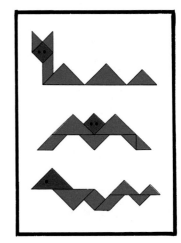

Page 15

0 1 2 3 4 5 6 7 8 9

Page 16 & 17

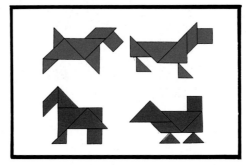

Page 18

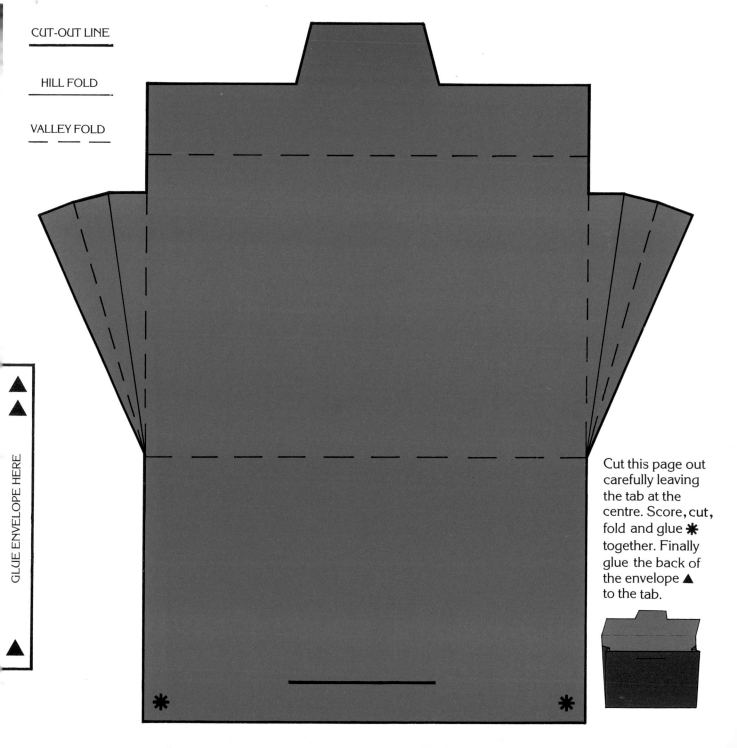

CUT-OUT LINE

HILL FOLD

VALLEY FOLD

GLUE ENVELOPE HERE

Cut this page out carefully leaving the tab at the centre. Score, cut, fold and glue ✱ together. Finally glue the back of the envelope ▲ to the tab.

KEEP YOUR TANGRAM PIECES HERE

GLUE TO TAB

Each Tangram shape has to be made from a complete set of seven pieces.
Do not mix different sizes or colours.